In Love

An anthology of love poems

In Love

An anthology of love poems

Poems selected by
JENNIFER CURRY

METHUEN

FOR TYM – OF COURSE!

This anthology first published in Great Britain 1989
by Methuen Children's Books
A Division of the Octopus Group Ltd
Michelin House, 81 Fulham Road, London SW3 6RB
Copyright for this anthology © 1989
by Methuen Children's Books
Typeset in Great Britain by
Poole Typesetting (Wessex) Ltd. Bournemouth, Dorset
Printed in Great Britain by
Redwood Burn Limited, Trowbridge, Wiltshire

ISBN 0 416 12782 7

Contents

Love Is
'A Singing Bird'

Love Lost
'First Ice'

Wedding Ways
'Flower and Bird and Wind and World'

Happy Endings
'The Right Human Face'

Last Word

Introduction

Love is a universal experience. So, practically every poet who ever wrote has written at least one love poem. When I began gathering together this collection I imagined it would be quite an easy task. All I had to do was find one hundred favourite poems which would reflect the nature of love in all its different moods, times and seasons. Nothing difficult about that, I thought.

I began with poems I had known and loved ever since I was twelve years old. My first two were by women, both suffused with joy – Elizabeth Barrett Browning's 'How Do I Love Thee?' and Christina Rossetti's 'A Birthday'. Robert Burns came next with the strong, singing simplicity of 'A Red, Red Rose'. Then I had to have something by my other favourite writers, John Donne and D. H. Lawrence, Thomas Hardy and W. B. Yeats. So far, so good.

But all these poets had been long dead. What were poets writing about love today, I wondered. That's when Roger McGough's wistful lament, 'Being-in-love', crept in, and Liz Hutchins' bitter 'She Said', in strong contrast to the dreamlike 'Milkmaid' by Laurie Lee and the radiance of George Mackay Brown's 'Country Girl'.

But all these poets were adults, skilled and mature, thoroughly grown-up. What were *young* writers saying about their own teenage experience, I asked myself. That's when I added sixteen-year-old Jon

Harley's rhapsody, 'Love So Surprise?', 'In and Out of Joyce's Daydream', by Darren Bowget, just fourteen, and the highly original 'A Time For Love' by Anna Pegler, another sixteen-year-old. . . .

And all this was nothing more than the tip of a vast mountain. My straightforward task had become a huge uphill marathon. After two months of reading and remembering I had collected almost five times as many poems as we had space for – and to my eyes, each one was a gem. So then, instead of happy gathering, I had to begin the painful process of throwing out. Eventually I managed to reduce my collection . . . but not to one hundred. It became totally stuck at one hundred and one! That's when the agony began. Losing that final poem really hurt me – it was like turning my back on a special friend.

The good news is that, if you enjoy this anthology, we hope to follow it up with *In Love Again*. And then my hundred and first poem will become the first of the new book. We would also like you to send us *your own* love poems. It is the fact that so much of the poetry in this collection has been written by children or teenagers that gives *In Love* its own particular quality. We would like to recapture that quality next time round, with *your* help. So, if you have written, or can write, a love poem that you think might be good enough to get into print, please send it to me, Jennifer Curry, at Methuen Children's Books, Michelin House, 81 Fulham Road, London SW3 6RB. I shall look forward to reading every single one.

JENNIFER CURRY

First Word

Brown Penny

I whispered, 'I am too young,'
And then, 'I am old enough';
Wherefore I threw a penny
To find out if I might love.
'Go and love, go and love, young man,
If the lady be young and fair.'
Ah, penny, brown penny, brown penny,
I am looped in the loops of her hair.

O love is the crooked thing,
There is nobody wise enough
To find out all that is in it,
For he would be thinking of love
Till the stars had run away
And the shadows eaten the moon.
Ah, penny, brown penny, brown penny,
One cannot begin it too soon.

W. B. YEATS

Awakening

'A Daisy-chain of Dreams'

Some Time

Some time! some time!
When will it be?
It might be winter,
It might be spring,
With snow on the ground
Or fruit on the tree,
Some time! some time!
When will it be?

Some one! some one!
What is he like?
Perhaps a coal-man,
Perhaps a king.
Will he come on a horse
Or a motor-bike?
Some one! some one!
What is he like?

Somewhere! somewhere!
Oh, but where?
In a hollow
Or on a height?
Over the water?
At the fair?
Somewhere! somewhere!
Oh, but where?

17

Some time! some time!
When will it be?
It might be morning,
It might be night,
With the sun in the sky
Or the moon on the sea –
Some time! some time!
When will it be?

ELEANOR FARJEON

Girls in a Factory

Seated in rows at the machines
Their heads are bent; the tacking needle
Stitches along the hours, along the seams.

What thoughts follow the needle
Over the fields of cloth,
Stitching into the seams
Perhaps a scarlet thread of love,
A daisy-chain of dreams?

DENIS GLOVER

Who Ever Felt as I!

Mother, I cannot mind my wheel;
My fingers ache, my lips are dry;
Oh! if you felt the pain I feel!
But oh, who ever felt as I!

SAPPHO
(7th Century BC)
Trans. from Greek by Walter Savage Landor

Milkmaid

The girl's far treble, muted to the heat,
calls like a fainting bird across the fields
to where her flock lies panting for her voice,
their black horns buried deep in marigolds.

They climb awake, like drowsy butterflies,
and press their red flanks through the tall
    branched grass,
and as they go their wandering tongues embrace
the vacant summer mirrored in their eyes.

Led to the limestone shadows of a barn
they snuff their past embalmèd in the hay,
while her cool hand, cupped to the udder's
    fount,
distils the brimming harvest of their day.

Look what a cloudy cream the earth gives out,
fat juice of buttercups and meadow-rye;
the girl dreams milk within her body's field
and hears, far off, her muted children cry.

LAURIE LEE

Kinky Hair Blues

Gwine find a beauty shop
Cause I ain't a belle.
Gwine find a beauty shop
Cause I ain't a lovely belle.
The boys pass me by,
They say I's not so swell.

See oder young gals
So slick and smart.
See dose oder young gals
So slick and smart.
I jes gwine die on de shelf
If I don't mek a start.

I hate dat ironed hair
And dat bleaching skin.
Hate dat ironed hair
And dat bleaching skin.
But I'll be all alone
If I don't fall in.

Lord 'tis you did gie me
All dis kinky hair.
'Tis you did gie me
All dis kinky hair,
And I don't envy gals
What got dose locks so fair.

Would You Believe It?

– Jacky's going out with Peter –
– Which one? NOT the one with spots –
– No of course not, Peter DAVIS –
– Don't believe you
        how d'you know? –
– Tracy told me but you mustn't say
I said so –
        course not
how did she find out? –
– Well,
Phillipa, that's Tracy's mate the one in 3G
her mate Mandy's sister Carol's
best friend Susan and her boyfriend
(his name's Peter)
saw them
        Coming Out The Pictures

(But you mustn't tell A SOUL
'cos Jacky's also going out
with someone else as well . . .

MICK GOWAR

25

First Date

When you race home from school,
  With your hair all askew,
You've loads of revision,
  And homework to do,
When all that is finished,
  You shampoo your hair,
Then dry it, and style it,
  With slow loving care,
You've barely got time,
  For a quick bite to eat,
Before you can change,
  Into something quite neat,
But it's got to look modern,
  And feminine too,
Then when you've changed,
  There's your make-up to do,
And now that your face,
  Is looking just right,
You glance in the mirror,
  Wow! what a sight!
He'll never resist you,
  You don't think he'll try,
Your heart beats loudly,
  Your spirits run high,
You look out the window,
  He's there at the gate,
And you hurry downstairs,
  To your very first date.

SUSAN WHYTE (15)

Shy Love

I remember that disco one Saturday night.
Suddenly seeing the girl for me.
There she sat in the corner like a radial piece
   of light.
Her eyes blue, her hair fair.

She turned around and stared at me.
Her eyes were dazzling and lips were
   flushed.
My heart beat faster
My legs were frozen like a block of ice.

She broke loose from the corner,
And came out fighting on the bell,
And pounded me with her words,
She so forward,
And I so shy.

Then I stunned her.
She fell for the fatal blow,
How she wobbled to and fro.
There she stood, gloves down.
The question came out again,
'Do you want to dance?' I said.

PAUL NICE (14)

27

Diane

Tired and dejected hair dripping
wet trying to hitch a ride
up Loch Lomondside. Her mini
stops short, a shaking wheezing
white terrier. I stare in
surprise I've waited nearly four
hours for this moment. 'Cumonn.
Gerrin.' She drawls we jerk
off and smash puddles northwards.

'Road's crawling with bloody
hitchers' she complains, 'but
I liked the tired way you
smiled.' We talk, she teaches
poetry in Australia, I read
her some of mine, she's impressed.
Wow! The gorgeous doll's impressed!

Tired now but laughing still
we tumble over to Skye
I fall asleep and talk
all night she listens
and cackles evilly into
her cornflakes tantalising
me with what I might
or might not have said.

Then out on the road to laugh
uproariously round the island
the car barking and yelping
with glee cocking its leg
at passing places nipping the
heels of lumbering buses. Screech
of brakes and out she leaps
sprinting up the drunken
road sandals flapping bangles
clinking mad hoops flying
round her pants. 'You crazy
kite you can't catch sheep!
It's not allowed!' Chokes back
into the driving seat 'I only
wanted to FEEL him!'

Zoom back to the caravan
fling her psychedelic suitcase
into the panting car. Swop
'phone numbers – world apart
yet nearer than that. A last
whoop of laughter as she unleashes
the mini and they chase bumble
bees to the ferry together. Some
times I wish I'd kissed her.

STEWART MCINTOSH

29

A Thunderstorm in Town

She wore a new 'terra-cotta' dress,
And we stayed, because of the pelting storm,
Within the hansom's dry recess,
Though the horse had stopped; yea, motion-
    less
We sat on, snug and warm.

Then the downpour ceased, to my sharp sad
    pain
And the glass that had screened our forms
    before
Flew up, and out she sprang to her door:
I should have kissed her if the rain
Had lasted a minute more.

THOMAS HARDY

First kiss

Warm lips touch
Bodies close
First kiss
Bliss

STEPHANIE GIPSON (17)

First Love

'A Dizziness'

Lovely Tracey

Dear Tracey,
    I am sending
This letter to you
to show all my love
for you and care
and respect.
This letter is not
from Peter it is from
Someone in class
Two who cares and
loves you very much.
Perhaps one day
I may not like
you as much as I do
now so while you've
got some time to
show your love for
me just use it.
Don't be shy to say
it if you do I
will be really glad
to know that you
love me. I have
only one thing to
say in nearly
everything I do I
always think of you
my beautiful girl.
    From *David*

DAVID PHIPPS (9)

First Love

I ne'er was struck before that hour
With love so sudden and so sweet.
Her face it bloomed like a sweet flower
And stole my heart away complete.
My face turned pale as deadly pale,
My legs refused to walk away,
And when she looked 'what could I ail?'
My life and all seemed turned to clay.

And then my blood rushed to my face
And took my sight away.
The trees and bushes round the place
Seemed midnight at noonday.
I could not see a single thing,
Words from my eyes did start;
They spoke as chords do from the string,
And blood burnt round my heart.

Are flowers the winter's choice?
Is love's bed always snow?
She seemed to hear my silent voice
And love's appeal to know.
I never saw so sweet a face
As that I stood before:
My heart has left its dwelling-place
And can return no more.

JOHN CLARE

34

Love So Surprise?

When in the wind is the where?
With the blue-eyes, the you-eyes,
And with the so wind in your hair
So golden, so random surprise?

Whither your lips so red,
Which meet mine in when and in where?
What words my lips so said
So lost in the random-wind there?

So love-lost in purple heather, or
Who else in the world so fair
Or cheek so smooth, or law
Of Nature surprise in the care?

When the You and the wind in the
    heather
With me, lips, words of Us love?
Is Nature random, so together
The Us and the so clouds above?

Is love in your eyes, You so fair?
Above us the random cloud wise?
Whither the random when and the
    where?
My nature – love you – so surprise?

JON HARLEY (16)

35

Girl, Boy, Flower, Bicycle

This girl
Waits at the corner for
This boy
Freewheeling on his bicycle.
She holds
A flower in her hand
A gold flower
In her hands she holds
The sun.
With power between his thighs
The boy
Comes smiling to her
He rides
A bicycle that glitters like
The wind.
This boy this girl
They walk
In step with the wind
Arm in arm
They climb the level street
To where
Laid on the glittering handlebars
The flower
Is round and shining as
The sun.

M. K. JOSEPH

Actors

We were actors,
Playing a part
Trying a role,
Waiting for cues
From each other
To know what to say next.

Didn't want to upstage you
Make you fluff your lines;
The show must go on,
No matter what
That's what
all the old troupers say.

Our stumbling rehearsals
Those takeaways for two
Our moves blocked out
under the streetlights,
Till the curtain goes up
on tomorrow.

That first stage kiss
Without a script:
Eye to eye,
Hoping we'd never dry . . .
Can't remember the next line,
Is there a prompter nearby?

CHRISTOPHER MANN

37

Love is Like a Dizziness

O, Love, love, love!
Love is like a dizziness;
It winna let a poor body
Gang about his biziness!

JAMES HOGG

It Was the Time of Roses

It was not in the winter
Our loving lot was cast:
It was the time of roses—
We plucked them as we passed!

That churlish season never frowned
On early lovers yet!
O, no—the world was newly crowned
With flowers, when first we met.

'Twas twilight, and I bade you go,
But still you held me fast:
It was the time of roses—
We plucked them as we passed . . . .

THOMAS HOOD

In and Out of Joyce's Daydream

One and one is two,
Two and two is four,
Three and three are the times I
watched the weakness in your wandering eye
  waver
as lovers for the first times two kissed, without
  a care.
Two times two is four,
Three times three is the smoothness of
your skin is so sublime times nine is seventy-
  two days
now you have gone. I wanted to tell you how
  I, don't know the answer,
miss your loving gaze.
I stare at your empty seat.

'James! 12 times 11 is 132.'
'Yes miss' you.

DARREN BOWGET (14)

She Said

She said: — You were very nice, quiet and
  polite,
She said: — You were considerate, well brought
  up,
She said: — You were happy and kind,
She knows you live 200 miles away,
She just can't understand us.

She knows I don't see enough of you,
She certainly makes sure of that,
She said I think of you too much,
She just can't understand us.

She said phone calls were too frequent,
She said they must stop; then relented and
She said two calls a week was enough,
She said ten minutes is sufficient for any news
  you've got.
She listens in I know she does,
She just can't understand us.

She saw my exam results,
She said that was the limit,
She asked what was in your letters that made
  me so distant,
She reads them now – then gives them to me.
She said that was the only way to prevent it.
I said 'Prevent what?'
She said she didn't understand me.

40

She said my letters were to be approved at
    first,
She said she'd read then post them,
She said she would,
She said any arguments were in vain,
She said I was too young,
She said you'd get tired then what would I do
    – no qualifications no job,
She doesn't understand us.

She said she'd posted my letters,
She said you haven't written back,
You are getting them aren't you,
She said you would she said
She said – she lied.

She's hurting me,
She's hurting you and your family,
She said – she says – she has said,
She will say – she will say no longer!
She cried when I left!
I don't understand her.

LIZ HUTCHINS

from *Romeo and Juliet*

But, soft! what light through yonder window
    breaks?
It is the east, and Juliet is the sun!
Arise, fair sun, and kill the envious moon,
Who is already sick and pale with grief,
That thou her maid art far more fair than she:
Be not her maid, since she is envious;
Her vestal livery is but sick and green,
And none but fools do wear it; cast it off.
It is my lady; O, it is my love!
O, that she knew she were!
She speaks, yet she says nothing: what of
    that?
Her eye discourses, I will answer it.
I am too bold, 'tis not to me she speaks:
Two of the fairest stars in all the heaven,
Having some business, do entreat her eyes
To twinkle in their spheres till they return.
What if her eyes were there, they in her head?
The brightness of her cheek would shame
    those stars
As daylight doth a lamp; her eyes in heaven
Would through the airy region stream so
    bright
That birds would sing, and think it were not
    night.
See how she leans her cheek upon her hand!
O, that I were a glove upon that hand,
That I might touch that cheek!

WILLIAM SHAKESPEARE

Elegy

I wish I could.
I wish I could take
Her in my arms and say
'Don't Cry'.
I wish I could show that
I care,
Say what I mean,
Love as I do.

When my arms
Hang clumsy,
When my cheeks
Blush deep,
When my eyes
Falter,
Cry for me too.

KATIE-LOUISE THOMAS (14)

Today

Today I have tasted the rain,
walking alone and still warm with you.

Honey has dropped on my tongue.
My skin has grown tender, so new

it is scorching my clothes.
Will people guess why

I shrink from their touch?
I need to be differently dressed. My

bones flow your way like rivers,
ask for wrappings of silk,

for cumulus pillows and rainbows
to bathe in, and your skin, smoother than
  milk.

JANE WHITTLE

The First Day

I wish I could remember the first day,
First hour, first moment of your meeting me;
If bright or dim the season, it might be
Summer or winter for aught I can say.
So unrecorded did it slip away,
So blind was I to see and to foresee,
So dull to mark the budding of my tree
That would not blossom yet for many a May.

If only I could recollect it! Such
A day of days! I let it come and go
As traceless as a thaw of bygone snow.
It seemed to mean so little, meant so much!
If only now I could recall that touch,
First touch of hand in hand! – Did one but
    know!

CHRISTINA ROSSETTI

45

One Day

One day I fell in love.
It was just like a butterfly
Emerging from its chrysalis;
So beautiful, I cried.
It was a bite
Out of an apple,
So sweet its juice
Tasted like honey.
It was a tiny
Baby fist,
Clutching a strand of hair;
A golden thread.
It was a rainbow
Of more than seven colours,
Millions and millions.
One day I fell in love
And I grew wings;
I flew. Briefly
I was a bird,
An eagle, flying
Up and up.
One day, one smile
Meant more to me
Than the whole world.
One day, I sang.
All day, I sang.
But then
My butterfly died

And the apple grew old.
The fist let go of the thread,
The golden hair.
My rainbow
Shattered into
A myriad
Coloured pieces.
My wings
Disappeared,
And I fell
Down and down.
I couldn't
Even
Sing

Then,
One day,

I fell in love.

RACHAEL ANNE-MARIE NAYLOR (14)

Love Is

'A Singing Bird'

A Birthday

My heart is like a singing bird
Whose nest is in a watered shoot:
My heart is like an apple-tree
Whose boughs are bent with thickset fruit;
My heart is like a rainbow shell
That paddles in a halcyon sea;
My heart is gladder than all these
Because my love is come to me.

Raise me a dais of silk and down;
Hang it with vair and purple dyes;
Carve it in doves and pomegranates,
And peacocks with a hundred eyes;
Work it in gold and silver grapes,
In leaves and silver fleurs-de-lys;
Because the birthday of my life
Is come, my love is come to me.

CHRISTINA ROSSETTI

51

Sonnet

I
Through
Blue
Sky
Fly
To
You
Why?
Sweet
Love
Feet
Move
So
Slow.

ANON.

Cupid and Campaspe

Cupid and my Campaspe played
At cards for kisses, Cupid paid;
He stakes his quiver, bow, and arrows,
His mother's doves, and team of
    sparrows;
Loses them too; then, down he throws
The coral of his lip, the rose
Growing on's cheek (but none knows
    how);
With these, the crystal of his brow,
And then the dimple of his chin:
All these did my Campaspe win.
At last, he set her both his eyes;
She won, and Cupid blind did rise.
O Love! has she done this to thee?
What shall (alas!) become of me?

JOHN LYLY

53

The Hill

Breathless, we flung us on the windy hill,
Laughed in the sun, and kissed the lovely grass.
You said, 'Through glory and ecstacy we pass;
Wind, sun, and earth remain, the birds sing still,
When we are old, are old. . . .' 'And when we die
All's over that is ours; and life burns on
Through other lovers, other lips', said I,
'Heart of my heart, our heaven is now, is won!'

'We are Earth's best, that learnt her lesson here.
Life is our cry. We have kept the faith!' we said;
'We shall go down with unreluctant tread
Rose-crowned into the darkness!' Proud we were,
And laughed, that had such brave true things to
     say.
– And then you suddenly cried, and turned away.

RUPERT BROOKE

Love Without Hope

Love without hope, as when the young bird-catcher
Swept off his tall hat to the Squire's own daughter,
So let the imprisoned larks escape and fly
Singing about her head, as she rode by.

ROBERT GRAVES

54

The Shirt of a Lad

As I did the washing one day
Under the bridge at Aberteifi,
And a golden stick to drub it,
And my sweetheart's shirt beneath it—
A knight came by upon a charger,
Proud and swift and broad of shoulder,
And he asked if I would sell
The shirt of the lad that I loved well.

No, I said, I will not trade—
Not if a hundred pounds were paid;
Not if two hillsides I could keep
Full with wethers and white sheep;
Not if two fields full of oxen
Under yoke were in the bargain;
Not if the herbs of all LLanddewi,
Trodden and pressed, were offered to me—
Not for the likes of that I'd sell
The shirt of the lad that I love well.

ANON.
*Trans. from Welsh by
Anthony Conran.*

I Will Make You Brooches

I will make you brooches and toys for your delight
Of bird-song at morning and star-shine at night.
I will make a palace fit for you and me
Of green days in forests and blue days at sea.

I will make my kitchen, and you shall keep your
   room,
Where white flows the river and bright blows the
   broom,
And you shall wash your linen and keep your body
   white
In rainfall at morning and dewfall at night.

And this shall be for music when no one else is
   near,
The fine song for singing, the rare song to hear!
That only I remember, that only you admire,
Of the broad road that stretches and the roadside
   fire.

ROBERT LOUIS STEVENSON

The Glow-worm

Among all lovely things my Love had been;
Had noted well the stars, all flowers that grew
About her home; but she had never seen
A glow-worm, never one, and this I knew.

While riding near her home one stormy night
A single glow-worm did I chance to espy;
I gave a fervent welcome to the sight,
And from my horse I leapt; great joy had I.

Upon a leaf the glow-worm did I lay,
To bear it with me through the stormy night:
And, as before, it shone without dismay;
Albeit putting forth a fainter light.

When to the dwelling of my Love I came,
I went into the orchard quietly;
And left the glow-worm, blessing it by name,
Laid safely by itself, beneath a tree.

The whole next day, I hoped, and hoped with
     fear;
At night the glow-worm shone beneath the
     tree;
I led my Lucy to the spot, 'Look here,'
Oh! joy it was for her, and joy for me!

WILLIAM WORDSWORTH

A Time For Love

I love you

swinging	every second
wound up	ready to spring
moving	anti-clockwise
ringing	in my ears

I love you

waking	☐
working	☐
laughing	☐
drinking	☐
crying	☐
sleeping	☐
always	☐

Please tick   inside me

ANNA PEGLER (16)

58

Harlem Night Song

Come,
Let us roam the night together
Singing

I love you

Across
The Harlem roof-tops
Moon is shining.
Night sky is blue
Stars are great drops
Of golden dew.

Down the street
A band is playing.

I love you

Come,
Let us roam the night together
Singing.

LANGSTON HUGHES

The Passionate Shepherd to His Love

Come live with me and be my Love,
And we will all the pleasures prove
That hills and valleys, dales and fields,
Or woods or steepy mountain yields.

And we will sit upon the rocks,
And see the shepherds feed their flocks
By shallow rivers, to whose falls
Melodious birds sing madrigals.

And I will make thee beds of roses
And a thousand fragrant posies;
A cap of flowers, and a kirtle
Embroidered all with leaves of myrtle.

A gown made of the finest wool
Which from our pretty lambs we pull;
Fair-linèd slippers for the cold,
With buckles of the purest gold.

A belt of straw and ivy-buds
With coral clasps and amber studs:
And if these pleasures may thee move,
Come live with me and be my Love.

The shepherd swains shall dance and sing
For thy delight each May morning:
If these delights thy mind may move,
Then live with me and be my Love.

CHRISTOPHER MARLOWE

Rose

Red rose, red rhythmed rose,
Red tooth-mugged ripe rhythmed rose
Is pulsing, quick, on my rose-shelf.

The room seems full of petals,
Red, red, red rose petals, and
They sing upon the floor.
My eyes, perhaps, are petals:
Red with love, pulsating: petals.

O there is a young, blush, red rose
Vivid in my tooth-mug:
                no one has seen her
Save me:
        my eyes which, like rose's
Red eye, she brightens and bares.

JAMES LOXLEY (16)

Decorated for a Kiss

I come to her house for love with a basket of red
    petals.
Men-friend tell me what a fool to go to the girl
Come, man, come fish shark, strong white shark,
At midnight come fish golden snapper along the
    warm black rocks.
But I decide my mind and come to her for love.
Her dress is patterned with blue dragon-flies
She has put a red bead in each ear
Green lizards run in her eyes
Her body has the scent of sun-dried khus-khus
    grass
The sweet fibres she has put between the linen
    since midday
She has washed her mouth with milk
She has rubbed her lips with bay leaves
She has made her limbs clean with water from a
    green calabash
Now she offers me a few plums and palm-wine
    from a gourd of scarlet leather.

IAN MCDONALD

A Red, Red Rose

O my luve is like a red, red rose
That's newly sprung in June.
O, my luve is like the melodie,
That's sweetly play'd in tune.

As fair art thou, my bonnie lass,
So deep in luve am I,
And I will luve thee still, my dear,
Till a' the seas gang dry.

Till a' the seas gang dry, my dear,
And the rocks melt wi' the sun!
And I will love thee still, my dear,
While the sands o' life shall run.

And fare thee weel, my only luve,
And fare thee weel a while!
And I will come again, my luve,
Tho it were ten thousand mile!

ROBERT BURNS

My Little Lize

Who is de prutties' gal you say?
Oh, hush up man an go away.
Yo don't know w'at yo talkin bout;
Yo ought to go an fin' dat out.
De prutties' gal dat one can meet
Dat ever walk along de street;
I guess yo never seen my Lize;
If yo had seen her – bless yo eyes,
Yo would be sure to 'gree wid me,
Dat she's de sweetes' gal dat be.
Why man! where was yo all dis time,
Dat yo don't see dis gal of mine?
Her skin is black an smoode as silk;
Her teet' is jus' as white as milk;
Her hair is of dem fluffy kin',
Wid curls a-hangin, black and shine.
Her shape is such dat can't be beat;
So graceful, slender an so neat.
W'ene'er she turn her eyes on you,
Dey seem to strike yo t'rough an t'rough,
Dere's not a sweeter lookin face;
An lips dat mek yo feel to tas'e.
Her hands is small an so's her feet,
Wid such a pair of enkles neat!
W'en she goes out to tek a walk
She sets de people all to talk.
De gals dey envy her wid fear,
Dey feel so cheap w'en she is near.

64

De boys dey lif' dere hats an try
To win a smile as she pass by.
But w'at's de use o talkin' so;
An try such beauty here to show!
Yo better see wid yo own eyes
Dis sweet an lovely little Lize;
For if I try de evening t'rough,
I couldn't quite explain to you.

JAMES MARTINEZ

Madrigal

My Love in her attire doth show her wit,
It doth so well become her;
For every season she hath dressings fit,
For Winter, Spring, and Summer.
No beauty she doth miss
When all her robes are on:
  But Beauty's self she is
When all her robes are gone.

ANON.

Meeting at Night

The grey sea and the long black land;
And the yellow half-moon large and low;
And the startled little waves that leap
In fiery ringlets from their sleep,
As I gain the cove with pushing prow,
And quench its speed i' the slushy sand.

Then a mile of warm sea-scented beach;
Three fields to cross till a farm appears;
A tap at the pane, the quick sharp scratch
And blue spurt of a lighted match,
And a voice less loud, through its joys and
    fears,
Than the two hearts beating each to each!

ROBERT BROWNING

O You Among Women

When pails empty the last brightness
Of the well, at twilight-time,
And you are there among women —
O mouth of silence,
Will you come with me, when I sign,
To the far green wood, that fences
A lake inlaid with light?

To be there, O, lost in each other,
While day melts in airy water,
And the drake-headed pike — a shade
In the waves' pale stir!
For love is there, under the breath,
As a coy star is there in the quiet
Of the wood's blue eye.

F. R. HIGGINS

Love's Philosophy

The fountains mingle with the river
And the rivers with the Ocean,
The winds of Heaven mix for ever
With a sweet emotion;
Nothing in the world is single;
All things by a law divine
In one spirit meet and mingle.
Why not I with thine? –

See the mountains kiss high Heaven
And the waves clasp one another;
No sister-flower would be forgiven
If it disdained its brother;
And the sunlight clasps the earth
And the moonbeams kiss the sea:
What is all this sweet work worth
If thou kiss not me?

PERCY BYSSHE SHELLEY

from *The Princess*

'Now sleeps the crimson petal, now the white;
Nor waves the cypress in the palace walk;
Nor winks the gold fin in the porphyry font:
The fire-fly wakens: waken thou with me.

Now droops the milkwhite peacock like a
    ghost,
And like a ghost she glimmers on to me.

Now lies the Earth all Danaë to the stars,
And all thy heart lies open unto me.

Now slides the silent meteor on, and leaves
A shining furrow, as thy thoughts in me.

Now folds the lily all her sweetness up,
And slips into the bosom of the lake:
So fold thyself, my dearest, thou, and slip
Into my bosom and be lost in me.'

ALFRED, LORD TENNYSON

The Day Comes

Lain close all night:
The moon a steady breathless sail.
The coming light
Is frozen out of air.

My love says it cannot be the day—
The light must deceive—
The lark, crying in the air
It loves, lies to us.

Daylight as thin as this
I wish would never come.
We are recovered from the dark
To part and walk about again.

JEFFREY WAINWRIGHT

up into the silence

up into the silence the green
silence with a white earth in it

you will (kiss me) go

out into the morning the young
morning with a warm world in it

(kiss me) you will go

on into the sunlight the fine
sunlight with a firm day in it

you will go (kiss me

down into your memory and
a memory and memory

i) kiss me (will go)

e.e.cummings

The Telephone

'When I was just as far as I could walk
From here today,
There was an hour
All still
When leaning with my head against a flower
I heard you talk.
Don't say I didn't, for I heard you say –
You spoke from that flower on the window sill –
Do you remember what it was you said?'

'First tell me what it was you thought you heard.'

'Having found the flower and driven a bee away,
I leaned my head,
And holding by the stalk,
I listened and I thought I caught the word –
What was it? Did you call me by my name?
Or did you say –
Someone said "Come" – I heard it as I bowed.'

'I may have thought as much, but not aloud.'

'Well, so I came.'

ROBERT FROST

70

Love Lost

'First Ice'

First Ice

A girl freezes in a telephone booth.
In her draughty overcoat she hides
A face all smeared
In tears and lipstick.

She breathes on her thin palms.
Her fingers are icy. She wears earrings.

She'll have to go home alone, alone,
Along the icy street.

First ice. It is the first time.
The first ice of telephone phrases.

Frozen tears glitter on her cheeks –
The first ice of human hurt.

ANDREY VOZNESENSKY

Disillusion

Look at him, over there
Watch him turn his head and stare
I think he fancies me

See the way he turns around
See him look me up and down
I'm sure he fancies me

Look at his lovely jet black hair
I don't really like 'em fair
I just know he fancies me

He's coming over, aint he great
He's gonna ask me for a date
I knew he fancied me

Hang on just a minute though
He's heading straight for my
        mate Flo
And I thought he fancied me

Tara Flo, I'll go on home
I spose I really should have known
He didn't fancy me

I don't like un anyway
He's ugly
I don't fancy he   MAUREEN BURGE

74

So, We'll Go No More a Roving

So, we'll go no more a roving
So late into the night,
Though the heart be still as loving,
And the moon be still as bright.

For the sword outwears its sheath,
And the soul wears out the breast,
And the heart must pause to breathe,
And love itself have rest.

Though the night was made for loving,
And the day returns too soon,
Yet we'll go no more a roving
By the light of the moon.

GEORGE GORDON, LORD BYRON

I Gave You My Love

I gave you my love, not just any love
love that burnt into me like a fire,
O my God, woe to her who would give
deep, deep love to another woman's son.

But were you and I to meet on a moor,
with no pillow but the holly tree
since it is wont to be sharp and wounding,
I would put my own, love, under your head.

ANON.
*Trans. from Gaelic
by Derick Thomson*

Waiting for a Rose

He shopping-trolleyed his way
Through the cash till queue
And handed it to me in a
Waitrose bag
Crushed
Like an unwanted receipt
Of his refrigerated
Affections for me.

CATHERINE BURKINSHAW (16)

You Went Away

Suddenly, in my world of you,
You created time.
I walked about in its bitter lanes
Looking for whom I'd lost, afraid to go
    home.

You stole yourself and gave me this
Torturer for my friend
Who shows me gardens rotting in air
And tells me what I no longer understand.

The birds sing still in the apple trees,
But not in mine. I hear
Only the clock whose wintry strokes
Say, 'Now is now', the same lie over and
    over.

If I could kill this poem, sticking
My thin pen through its throat,
It would stand crying by your bed
And haunt your cruelty every empty night.

NORMAN MACCAIG

77

Manwatching

From across the party I watch you,
Watching her.
Do my possessive eyes
Imagine your silent messages?
I think not.
She looks across at you
And telegraphs her flirtatious reply.
I have come to recognize this code,
You are on intimate terms with this pretty
    stranger,
And there is nothing I can do,
My face is calm, expressionless,
But my eyes burn into your back.
While my insides shout with rage.
She weaves her way towards you,
Turning on a bewitching smile.
I can't see your face, but you are mesmerised I
    expect.
I can predict you: I know this scene so well,
Some acquaintance grabs your arm,

You turn and meet my accusing stare head on,
Her eyes follow yours, meet mine,
And then slide away, she understands,
She's not interested enough to compete.
It's over now.
She fades away, you drift towards me,
'I'm bored' you say, without a trace of guilt,
So we go.

Passing the girl in the hall.
'Bye' I say frostily,
I suppose
You winked.

GEORGIA GARRETT

Love Song – First Movement

I got your letter
The other day.
I see you won't be coming
I see you can't make it.
Well, I can't make it either
Not without you.

I kissed a girl, other day
And as I did so . . .
It was then I realised
How much I really missed you
I knew . . .
I should have been kissing YOU!

I cried that night.
I don't know what it is
But you're like no one else
I ever knew.
Can it be
Can it possibly be
I love you?

BRIAN ROBINSON

Being-in-love

you are so very beautiful
i cannot help admiring
your eyes so often sadnessful
and lips so kissinspiring

i think about my being-in-love
and touch the flesh you wear so well
i think about my being-in-love
and wish you were as well
                          as well
and wish you were as well

ROGER MCGOUGH

A Former Love

She grew from the crowd,
stepping, streaming along the pavement,
head tossed high,
hair longer than before.
She saw me,
swooped head to breast,
rushed past.

A scent hung in the air.

GILES GORDON

Love's Secret

Never seek to tell thy love,
Love that never told can be;
For the gentle wind doth move
Silently, invisibly.

I told my love, I told my love,
I told her all my heart,
Trembling, cold, in ghastly fears.
Ah! She did depart!

Soon after she was gone from me,
A traveller came by,
Silently, invisibly:
He took her with a sigh.

WILLIAM BLAKE

O Western Wind

O western wind, when wilt thou blow
That the small rain down can rain?
Christ, if my love were in my arms,
And I in my bed again.

ANON.

81

The Ballad of Camden Town

I walked with Maisie long years back
The streets of Camden Town,
I splendid in my suit of black,
And she divine in brown.

Hers was a proud and noble face,
A secret heart, and eyes
Like water in a lonely place
Beneath unclouded skies.

A bed, a chest, a faded mat,
And broken chairs a few,
Were all we had to grace our flat
In Hazel Avenue.

But I could walk to Hampstead Heath,
And crown her head with daisies,
And watch the streaming world beneath,
And men with other Maisies.

When I was ill and she was pale
And empty stood our store,
She left the latchkey on its nail,
And saw me nevermore.

Perhaps she cast herself away
Lest both of us should drown.
Perhaps she feared to die, as they
Who die in Camden Town.

What came of her? The bitter nights
Destroy the rose and lily,
And souls are lost among the lights
Of painted Piccadilly.

What came of her? The river flows
So deep and wide and stilly,
And waits to catch the fallen rose
And clasp the broken lily.

I dream she dwells in London still
And breathes the evening air,
And often walk to Primrose Hill,
And hope to meet her there.

Once more together we will live,
For I will find her yet:
I have so little to forgive;
So much I can't forget.

JAMES ELROY FLECKER

With You

Being without you
Leaves me empty and hollow
Like a sky with no clouds or sun or moon
With you I was someone
My own special person
When you left you took something I thought
    was mine
What you gave me
Was something new to live with
An eternal waiting that hurts inside me

But knowing that you are with someone else
Is hurting me even more.

CATHERINE WILKINSON (13)

Love Note

when I know you're going away
I miss you before you've even gone

ADRIAN MITCHELL

84

To His Love

He's gone, and all our plans
Are useless indeed.
We'll walk no more on Cotswold
Where the sheep feed
Quietly and take no heed.

His body that was so quick
Is not as you
Knew it, on Severn river
Under the blue
Driving our small boat through.

You would not know him now . . .
But still he died
Nobly, so cover him over
With violets of pride
Purple from Severn side.

Cover him, cover him soon!
And with thick-set
Masses of memoried flowers —
Hide that red wet
Thing I must somehow forget.

IVOR GURNEY

What She Said

Before I laughed with him
    nightly,

    the slow waves beating
    on his wide shores
    and the palmyra
    bringing forth heron-like flowers
    near the waters,

my eyes were like the lotus
my arms had the grace of the bamboo
my forehead was mistaken for the moon.

But now

MATURAI ERUTTĀLAN CĒNTAMPŪTAN
(2nd century AD)

Trans. from Tamil by
A. K. Ramanujan

Lost Summers

There is too much rain washing away experience.
I must remember summer,
Lying under hedgerows,
Paper pink-for-a-day dogroses
The blanched mouths of June eager for love.
Ripe grass, green, dark with bruises.
Down on your cheek, fuzzed gold in sunshine.
Astonishing cool smoothness of skin
The small rake's teeth of eyelashes
Kisses, gentle as slow running water.
I must remember summer.

ROBERT SPARROW

The Night has a Thousand Eyes

The night has a thousand eyes,
And the day but one;
Yet the light of the bright world dies
With the dying sun.

The mind has a thousand eyes,
And the heart but one;
Yet the light of a whole life dies
When love is done.

FRANCIS WILLIAM BOURDILLON

Wedding Ways

'Flower and Bird and Wind and World'

To the Virgins,
to Make Much of Time

Gather ye rosebuds while ye may,
Old time is still a-flying:
And this same flower that smiles today
Tomorrow will be dying.

The glorious lamp of heaven, the sun,
The higher he's a-getting,
The sooner will his race be run,
And nearer he's to setting.

That age is best which is the first,
When youth and blood are warmer;
But being spent, the worse, and worst
Times still succeed the former.

Then be not coy, but use your time,
And while ye may, go marry:
For having lost but once your prime,
You may for ever tarry.

ROBERT HERRICK

91

The Riddling Knight

There were three sisters fair and bright,
Jennifer, Gentle and Rosemary,
And they three loved one valiant knight-
As the dove flies over the mulberry-tree.

The eldest sister let him in,
And barr'd the door with a silver pin.

The second sister made his bed,
And placed soft pillows under his head.

The youngest sister that same night
Was resolved for to wed wi' this valiant
    knight.

'And if you can answer questions three,
O then, fair maid, I'll marry wi' thee.

'Or what is louder nor a horn,
Or what is sharper nor a thorn?

'O what is heavier nor the lead,
Or what is better nor the bread?

'Or what is longer nor the way,
Or what is deeper nor the sea?' –

'O shame is louder nor a horn,
And hunger is sharper nor a thorn.

'O sin is heavier nor the lead,
The blessing's better nor the bread.

'O the wind is longer nor the way
And love is deeper nor the sea.'

'You have answer'd aright my questions
    three',
Jennifer, Gentle and Rosemary;
'And now, fair maid, I'll marry wi' thee',
As the dove flies over the mulberry-tree.

ANON.

The Maidens Came

The maidens came
When I was in my mother's bower,
I had all that I wold.
The bailie beareth the bell away,
The lily, the rose, the rose I lay.

The silver is white,
Red is the gold,
The robes they lay in fold.
The bailie beareth the bell away,
The lily, the rose, the rose I lay.

And through the glass window
Shines the sun.
How should I love and I so young?
The bailie beareth the bell away,
The lily, the rose, the rose I lay.

ANON.

Down in Yonder Meadow

Down in yonder meadow where the green grass
    grows,
Pretty Pollie Pillicote bleaches her clothes.
She sang, she sang, she sang, oh, so sweet,
She sang, *Oh, come over!* across the street.
He kissed her, he kissed her, he bought her a
    gown,
A gown of rich cramasie out of the town.
He bought her a gown and a guinea gold ring,
A guinea, a guinea, a guinea gold ring;
Up street, and down, shine the windows made
    of glass,
Oh, isn't Pollie Pillicote a braw young lass?
Cherries in her cheeks, and ringlets her hair,
Hear her singing *Handy, Dandy* up and down the
    stair.

TRADITIONAL SINGING GAME RHYME

The River-Merchant's Wife:
A Letter

While my hair was still cut straight across my
    forehead
I played about the front gate, pulling flowers.
You came by on bamboo stilts, playing horse,
You walked about my seat, playing with blue
    plums.
And we went on living in the village of Chokan:
Two small people, without dislike or suspicion.

At fourteen I married My Lord you.
I never laughed, being bashful.
Lowering my head, I looked at the wall.
Called to, a thousand times, I never looked back.

At fifteen I stopped scowling,
I desired my dust to be mingled with yours
Forever and forever and forever.
Why should I climb the look out?

At sixteen you departed,
You went into far Ku-to-yen, by the river of
    swirling eddies,
And you have been gone five months.
The monkeys make sorrowful noise overhead.

You dragged your feet when you went out.
By the gate now, the moss is grown, the differ-
    ent mosses,
Too deep to clear them away!
The leaves fall early this autumn, in wind.
The paired butterflies are already yellow with
    August
Over the grass in the West garden;
They hurt me. I grow older.
If you are coming down through the narrows of
    the river Kiang,
Please let me know beforehand,
And I will come out to meet you
        As far as Cho-fu-Sa.

LI PO *(8th Century)*
Trans. from Chinese by
EZRA POUND

Epithalamion

Singing, today I married my white girl
beautiful in a barley field.
Green on thy finger a grass blade curled,
so with this ring I thee wed, I thee wed,
and send our love to the loveless world
of all the living and all the dead.

Now, no more than vulnerable human,
we, more than one, less than two,
are nearly ourselves in a barley field –
and only love is the rent that's due
though the bailiffs of time return anew
to all the living but not the dead.

Shipwrecked, the sun sinks down harbours
of a sky, unloads its liquid cargoes
of marigolds, and I and my white girl
lie still in the barley – who else wishes
to speak, what more can be said
by all the living against all the dead?

Come then all you wedding guests:
green ghost of trees, gold of barley,
you blackbird priests in the field,
you wind that shakes the pansy head
fluttering on a stalk like a butterfly;
come the living and come the dead.

Listen flowers, birds, winds, worlds,
tell all today that I married
more than a white girl in the barley –
for today I took to my human bed
flower and bird and wind and world,
and all the living and all the dead.

DANNIE ABSE

Proud Maisie

Proud Maisie is in the wood,
Walking so early;
Sweet Robin sits on the bush,
Singing so rarely.

'Tell me, thou bonny bird,
When shall I marry me?'
'When six braw gentlemen
Kirkward shall carry ye.'

'Who makes the bridal bed,
Birdie, say truly?'
'The grey-headed sexton
That delves the grave duly.'

'The glowworm o'er grave and stone
Shall light thee steady;
The owl from the steeple sing
Welcome, proud lady.'

SIR WALTER SCOTT

Wedding Wind

The wind blew all my wedding-day,
And my wedding-night was the night of the high
    wind;
And a stable door was banging, again and again,
That he must go and shut it, leaving me
Stupid in candlelight, hearing rain,
Seeing my face in the twisted candlestick,
Yet seeing nothing. When he came back
He said the horses were restless, and I was sad
That any man or beast that night should lack
The happiness I had.

    Now in the day
All's ravelled under the sun by the wind's
    blowing.
He has gone to look at the floods, and I
Carry a chipped pail to the chicken-run,
Set it down, and stare. All is the wind
Hunting through clouds and forests, thrashing
My apron and the hanging cloths on the line.
Can it be borne, this bodying-forth by wind
Of joy my actions turn on, like a thread
Carrying beads? Shall I be let to sleep
Now this perpetual morning shares my bed?
Can even death dry up
These new delighted lakes, conclude
Our kneeling as cattle by all-generous waters?

                              PHILIP LARKIN

101

Cotton

My wedding-gown's cotton,
My wedding-gown's cheap,
It's crisper than sea-foam
And whiter than sheep,
Printed with daisies
In yellow and green,
A prettier wedding-gown
Never was seen!
Light-heart and light-foot
I'll walk into church
As straight and as slim
As a silvery birch,
And after my wedding
I never will lay
Like ladies my wedding-gown
Lightly away.
I'll wash it in soapsuds
As fresh as when new,
And rinse it in rainwater
Softer than dew,
And peg it on Saturdays
High on the line,
And wear it on Sundays
Full of sunshine.

My wedding-gown's cotton,
It cost me a crown.
Was ever girl wed in
A commoner gown? –
As birds in the branches,
As flowers on the green,
The commonest wedding-gown
Ever was seen!

ELEANOR FARJEON

Green

The dawn was apple-green,
The sky was green wine held up in the sun,
The moon was a golden petal between.

She opened her eyes, and green
They shone, clear like flowers undone
For the first time, now for the first time seen.

D. H. LAWRENCE

103

Sonnet 116

Let me not to the marriage of true mindes
Admit impediments,love is not love
Which alters when it alteration findes,
Or bends with the remover to remove.
O no, it is an ever fixed marke
That lookes on tempests and is never shaken;
It is the star to every wandering barke,
Whose worth's unknowne, although his height
    be taken.
Love's not Time's foole, though rosie lips and
    cheeks
Within his bending sickle's compasse come,
Love alters not with his breefe houres and
    weekes,
But beares it out even to the edge of doome:
If this be error and upon me proved,
I never writ, nor no man ever loved.

WILLIAM SHAKESPEARE

For M. and R.

I wish you

The last strawberry of summer,
An umbrella-shared ice-cream in the rain,
A warm bed on a cold night,
A rainbow over slate-grey moorland.

A dragon-fly's sapphire hover,
Starlit seashore evenings,
Waking sunlight through shutters,
The long embrace that stills pain.

Fountains of laughter,
A slow song on an empty dance-floor,
Airport reunions and railway-station
    partings,
Long-distance late-night phone calls.

Audiences of one among a thousand,
Cold wine on a terrace at dusk,
Moments in the dark when only movement
    speaks,
And the perfect-pitched harmony
        of an eternal duet.

CHRISTOPHER MANN

Happy Endings

'The Right Human Face'

My True Love hath my Heart . . .

My true love hath my heart, and I have his,
By just exchange one for the other given.
I hold his dear, and mine he cannot miss;
There never was a better bargain driven.
His heart in me keeps me and him in one;
My heart in him his thoughts and senses
   guides;
He loves my heart, for once it was his own;
I cherish his, because in me it bides.
His heart his wound receivèd from my sight;
My heart was wounded with his wounded
   heart;
For as from me on him his hurt did light
So still methought in me his hurt did smart:
Both equal hurt, in this change sought our
   bliss;
My true love hath my heart, and I have his.

SIR PHILIP SIDNEY

Strawberries

There were never strawberries
like the ones we had
that sultry afternoon
sitting on the step
of the open french window
facing each other
your knees held in mine
the blue plates in our laps
the strawberries glistening
in the hot sunlight
we dipped them in sugar
looking at each other
not hurrying the feast
for one to come
the empty plates
laid on the stone together
with the two forks crossed
and I bent towards you
sweet in that air
in my arms
abandoned like a child
from your eager mouth
the taste of strawberries
in my memory
lean back again
let me love you
let the sun beat

on our forgetfulness
one hour of all
the heat intense
and summer lightning
on the Kilpatrick hills

let the storm wash the plates

EDWIN MORGAN

Country Girl

I make seven circles, my love
For your good breaking.
I make the gray circle of bread
And the circle of ale
And I drive the butter round in a
   golden ring
And I dance when you fiddle
And I turn my face with the turning
   sun till your feet come in from the
   field.
My lamp throws a circle of light,
Then you lie for an hour in the hot
   unbroken circle of my arms.

GEORGE MACKAY BROWN

111

Song

O wert thou in the storm
How I would shield thee:
To keep thee dry and warm,
A camp I would build thee.

Though the clouds pour'd again,
Not a drop should harm thee,
The music of wind, and rain,
Rather should charm thee.

O wert thou in the storm,
A shed I would build thee;
To keep thee dry and warm, –
How I would shield thee.

The rain should not wet thee,
Nor thunder clap harm thee.
By thy side I would sit me, –
To comfort, and warm thee.

I would sit by thy side, love,
While the dread storm was over; –
And the wings of an angel
My charmer would cover.

JOHN CLARE

How Do I Love Thee?

How do I love thee? Let me count the ways.
I love thee to the depth and breadth and
  height
My soul can reach, when feeling out of sight
For the ends of Being and ideal Grace.
I love thee to the level of everyday's
Most quiet need, by sun and candle-light.
I love thee freely, as men strive for Right;
I love thee purely, as they turn from Praise.
I love thee with the passion put to use
In my old griefs, and with my childhood's
  faith.
I love thee with a love I seemed to lose
With my lost saints, – I love thee with the
  breath,
Smiles, tears, of all my life! – and, if God
  choose,
I shall but love thee better after death.

ELIZABETH BARRETT BROWNING

from *The Song of Solomon*

I am the rose of Sharon, and the lily of the valleys.

As the lily among thorns, so is my love among the
daughters.

As the apple tree among the trees of the wood, so
is my beloved among the sons. I sat down under
his shadow with great delight, and his fruit was
sweet to my taste.

He brought me to the banqueting house, and his
banner over me was love.

Stay me with flagons, comfort me with apples: for I
am sick of love.

His left hand is under my head, and his right hand
doth embrace me.

I charge you, O ye daughters of Jerusalem, by the
roes, and by the hinds of the field, that ye stir
not up, nor awake my love, till he please.

The voice of my beloved! behold, he cometh leaping
upon the mountains, skipping upon the hills.

My beloved is like a roe or a young hart: behold,
he standeth behind our wall, he looketh forth at
the windows, showing himself through the
lattice.

My beloved spake, and said unto me, Rise up, my
love, my fair one, and come away.

For, lo, the winter is past, the rain is over and
gone;

114

The flowers appear on the earth; the time of the
 singing of birds is come, and the voice of the
 turtle is heard in our land:
The fig tree putteth forth her green figs, and the
 vines with the tender grape give a good smell.
 Arise, my love, my fair one, and come away.
O my dove, that art in the clefts of the rock, in the
 secret places of the stairs, let me see thy
 countenance, let me hear thy voice; for sweet is
 thy voice, and thy countenance is comely.
Take us the foxes, the little foxes, that spoil the
 vines: for our vines have tender grapes.
My beloved is mine, and I am his: he feedeth
 among the lilies.
Until the day break, and the shadows flee away,
 turn, my beloved, and be thou like a roe or a
 young hart upon the mountains of Bether.

Sonnet 18

Shall I compare thee to a Summer's day?
Thou art more lovely and more temperate:
Rough windes do shake the darling buds of
    Maie,
And Summer's lease hath all too short a date:
Sometimes too hot the eye of heaven shines,
And often is his gold complexion dimm'd,
And every faire from faire some-time declines,
By chance, or nature's changing course
    untrim'd:
But thy eternall Summer shall not fade,
Nor loose possession of that faire thou ow'st,
Nor shall death brag thou wandr'st in his
    shade,
When in eternall lines to time thou grow'st,
So long as men can breathe or eyes can see,
So long lives this, and this gives life to thee.

WILLIAM SHAKESPEARE

Gloire de Dijon

When she rises in the morning
I linger to watch her;
She spreads the bath-cloth underneath the
    window
And the sunbeams catch her
Glistening white on the shoulders,
While down her sides the mellow
Golden shadow glows as
She stoops to the sponge, and her swung
    breasts
Sway like full-blown yellow
Gloire de Dijon roses.

She drips herself with water, and her
    shoulders
Glisten as silver, they crumple up
Like wet and falling roses, and I listen
For the sluicing of their rain-dishevelled petals.
In the window full of sunlight
Concentrates her golden shadow
Fold on fold, until it glows as
Mellow as the glory roses.

D. H. LAWRENCE

The Sun Rising

Busy old fool, unruly Sun,
Why dost thou thus,
Through windows, and through curtains call on
   us?
Must to thy motions lovers' seasons run?
Saucy pedantic wretch, go chide
Late school-boys, and sour 'prentices,
Go tell court-huntsmen that the King will ride,
Call country ants to harvest offices;
Love, all alike, no season knows, nor clime,
Nor hours, days, months, which are the rags of
   time.

Thy beams, so reverend, and strong
Why shouldst thou think?
I could eclipse and cloud them with a wink,
But that I would not lose her sight so long:
If her eyes have not blinded thine,
Look, and tomorrow late, tell me,
Whether both the Indias of spice and mine
Be where thou left'st them, or lie here with me.
Ask for those kings whom thou saw'st yesteday,
And thou shalt hear, 'All here in one bed lay.'

She is all States, and all Princes, I;
Nothing else is.
Princes do but play us; compar'd to this,
All honour's mimic; all wealth alchemy.
Thou Sun art half as happy as we,
In that the world's contracted thus;
Thine age asks ease, and since thy duties be
To warm the world, that's done in warming us.
Shine here to us, and thou art every where;
This bed thy centre is, these walls, thy sphere.

JOHN DONNE

Reasons

Sweet one I love you
for your lovely shape,
for the art you make
in paint and bed and rhyme,
but most because we see
into each other's hearts,
there to read secrets
and to trust,
and cancel time.

TOM MCGRATH

119

Willowherb

Willowherb it was
and as we pushed so gently
through the swollen bank
of pink and feather
the airborne seeds
made us their moving target.

Running only sucked them down
in our air-wake
and they soon found our hair,
our skin,
our folded fingers.

And our love took them in
and kept them in its sacred place,
the womb where willowherb
and all the flowers of Summer
are made to grow for us.

BARRY NORRINGTON

Is Right

I am a cat
the sun is stroking
since your visit.

Purring
as I walk the garden
I can love it

you and me
the flowers and trees
the way she rolls

and lets the light
expose her gently,
lets the breeze

explore her fields.
She curls her paws
the way I breathe

and smile to feel
this place, this time
this once, is right.

JANE WHITTLE

121

The Confirmation

Yes, yours, my love, is the right human face.
I in my mind had waited for this long,
Seeing the false and searching for the true,
Then found you as a traveller finds a place
Of welcome suddenly amid the wrong
Valleys and rocks and twisting roads. But you,
What shall I call you? A fountain in a waste,
A well of water in a country dry,
Or anything that's honest and good, an eye
That makes the whole world bright. Your open
   heart,
Simple with giving, gives the primal deed,
The first good world, the blossom, the blowing
   seed,
The hearth, the steadfast land, the wandering
   sea,
Not beautiful or rare in every part,
But like yourself, as they were meant to be.

EDWIN MUIR

Love Comes Quietly

Love comes quietly,
finally, drops
about me, on me,
in the old ways.

What did I know
thinking myself
able to go
alone all the way.

ROBERT CREELEY

Last Word

When You are Old

When you are old and grey and full of sleep
And nodding by the fire, take down this book;
And slowly read, and dream of the soft look
Your eyes had once, and of their shadows
   deep;

How many loved your moments of glad grace,
And loved your beauty with love false or true;
But one man loved the pilgrim soul in you,
And loved the sorrows of your changing face;

And bending down beside the glowing bars,
Murmur, a little sadly, how love fled
And paced upon the mountains overhead,
And hid his face amid a crowd of stars.

W. B. YEATS

Index of Poets

Index of first lines

131

Acknowledgements

Epithalamion © Dannie Abse, reprinted by permission of Anthony Sheil Associates on behalf of Dannie Abse.

Love Without Hope by Robert Graves is reprinted from *Robert Graves' Collected Poems* by permission of A. P. Watt Limited on behalf of The Executors of the Estate of Robert Graves.

Diane © Stewart Macintosh, reprinted by permission of the Edinburgh University Press.

up into the silence the green by e. e. cummings, from *Complete Poems by e. e. cummings*, by permission of Grafton Books, a division of the Collins Publishing Group, and Liveright Publishing Corporation.

Plucking the Rushes from *170 Chinese Poems* translated by Arthur Waley, reprinted by permission of Constable Publishers.

Strawberries by Edwin Morgan, from *Poems of Thirty Years* (1982), Edwin Morgan, reprinted by permission of Carcanet Press Limited.

The Day Comes by Jeffrey Wainwright, from *Selected Poems* (1985) by Jeffrey Wainright, reprinted by permission of Carcanet Press Limited.

Peter Owen, London, and reprinted by permission of the publisher.

Willowherb © Barry Norrington, reprinted from *Stolen Time* by permission of the author.

Lost Summers by Robert Sparrow, copyright reserved; reprinted by permission of the author.

Salcombe (1948) © Gareth Owen 1985, from *Song of the City* by Gareth Owen, reprinted by permission of William Collins Sons & Co. Ltd.

Would You Believe It © Mick Gowar 1981, from *Swings and Roundabouts* by Mick Gowar, reprinted by permission of William Collins Sons & Co. Ltd.

The Telephone by Robert Frost, from *The Poetry of Robert Frost*, edited by Edward Connery Lathem, and reprinted by permission of the Estate of Robert Frost, the editor, and Jonathan Cape Ltd.

Love Note by Adrian Mitchell, reprinted from *For Beauty Douglas* © Adrian Mitchell 1982, by permission of WH Allen Publishers.

Being In Love by Roger McGough, from *Summer with Monica*, published by Andre Deutsch Ltd, and reprinted by permission of the Peters Fraser & Dunlop Ltd.

Footsteps by Catherine Burkinshaw, *Shy Love* by Paul Nice, *Love So Surprise?* by Jon Harley, *In & Out of Joyce's Daydream* by Darren Bowget, *One Day* by Rachel Anne-Marie Naylor, *A Time For Love* by Anna Pegler, *Rose* by James Loxley, *Waiting For A Rose* by Catherine Burkinshaw, *With You* by Catherine Wilkinson, and *Elegy* by Katie-Louise Thomas, all reprinted by permission of Cadbury's National Exhibition of Children's Art – Poetry Section.

Every effort has been made to trace all the copyright holders and the publishers apologise if any inadvertent omission has been made.